Join in —
Jump on!

Scripture Union
207-209 Queensway, Bletchley, Milton Keynes, MK2 2EB, UK

Writers: Sarah Bell, Margaret Cluley, Jean Elliott, Marjory Francis, Susanne and Mark Hopkins
Editor: Marjory Francis
Design: Chris Gander Design Associates   Illustration: Branwen Thomas

ISBN 185999 3222
© Scripture Union 1999

Printed and bound in the UK by Ebenezer Baylis & Son Ltd, The Trinity Press,
Worcester and London

To help you

Did you know the Bible is made up of lots of books?

You will be reading from these books in **Join in – Jump on!**
Genesis 1 Kings 2 Kings Psalms
See if you can find them in the Old Testament books below and colour them in.

Genesis | Exodus | Leviticus | Numbers | Deuteronomy | Joshua | Judges | Ruth | 1 Samuel | 2 Samuel | 1 Kings | 2 Kings | 1 Chronicles | 2 Chronicles | Ezra | Nehemiah | Esther | Job | Psalms | Proverbs | Ecclesiastes | Song of Songs | Lamentations | Isaiah | Jeremiah | Ezekiel | Daniel | Hosea | Joel | Amos | Obadiah | Jonah | Micah | Nahum | Habakkuk | Zephaniah | Haggai | Zechariah | Malachi

Now see if you can find and colour the ones you will be reading from the New Testament:
Luke John Acts Philippians Ephesians

Matthew | Mark | Luke | John | Acts | Romans | 1 Corinthians | 2 Corinthians | Galatians | Ephesians | Philippians | Colossians | 1 Thessalonians | 2 Thessalonians | 1 Timothy | 2 Timothy | Titus | Philemon | Hebrews | James | 1 Peter | 2 Peter | 1 John | 2 John | 3 John | Jude | Revelation

In this book find out about:

Jesus meets sad and lonely people *Days 1 to 6*
Jacob *Days 7 to 11*
Paul becomes a Christian *Days 12 to 13*
Paul's adventures *Days 14 to 19*
All about sheep *Days 20 to 23*
Elijah by the river *Days 24 to 27*
Elijah on the mountains *Days 28 to 31*
Stories Jesus told *Days 32 to 37*
Elisha's poor friends *Days 38 to 40*
Elisha's rich friends *Days 41 to 44*
I can pray to God *Days 45 to 48*
Paul writes letters *Days 49 to 50*

Plus:
Lots of Extra pages
All over the world!
The joke and puzzle page!

How to use this book

There are Bible activities in this book to keep you busy for 50 days. You will find stories about people in the Bible and lots of ideas to help you get to know God better. Each day you will find
- something to read
- a puzzle or questions to answer
- something to look up in the Bible
- a prayer idea

Sometimes there are Extra fun ideas too!

Here are some ideas for using **Join in – Jump on!**
- It's best to read it every day if you can, but it doesn't matter if you miss days sometimes. Just carry on from where you got up to.
- It's OK to use **Join in – Jump on!** on your own, or you might like someone to help you.
- Most days you will just need a Bible and a pencil to use with **Join in – Jump on!**
- It's best to save the Extra pages for when you have lots of time. You will need to collect other things to use for these.
- Try to find somewhere quiet to read your Bible and **Join in – Jump on!**

So make sure you have a Bible and a pencil, and jump on to **Join in – Jump on!** now!

Jesus meets sad and lonely people

Have you ever had an illness with itchy spots? I'm sure you were glad when they went away again. The men in our story today had an illness where the spots didn't go away. Worse still, the men couldn't live at home anymore because no one else wanted to catch their disease. They felt sad and lonely until one day they met Jesus.

Read about them in **Luke chapter 17, verses 11 to 14**.

What did Jesus tell them to do? (verse 14) "Go to the p r i e s t s."

This meant they were better! The priests would tell them they could go back home.

prayer time

How do you think the men felt now? Draw the face of one of them.

When people are ill they often feel sad and lonely. Think of someone you know who isn't very well. Ask Jesus to help and comfort them.

Jesus meets sad and lonely people

Remember the men who have met Jesus and been healed?
Here they are again.

Read the rest of their story in **Luke chapter 17, verses 15 to 19**.

What did one man do that was different from the others?

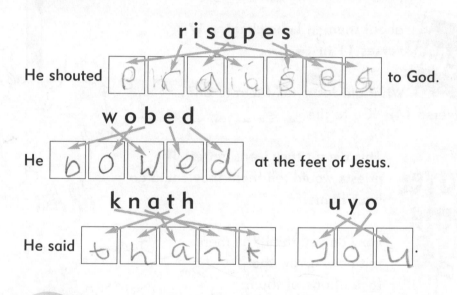

r i s a p e s

He shouted | p | r | a | i | s | e | s | to God.

w o b e d

He | b | o | w | e | d | at the feet of Jesus.

k n a t h   u y o

He said | t | h | a | n | t | | y | o | u |.

prayer time

It's easy to forget to say "Thank you", but it makes so much difference. Why don't you think of as many things as you can that you want to thank Jesus for?

Jesus meets sad and lonely people

Read **Luke chapter 6, verses 6 and 7** in your Bible. Some of the words might be new to you. Write down any unusual words here:

....

....

....

Ask an adult to help you understand what they mean.

There were 39 things the Jewish people weren't allowed to do on the Sabbath Day! Picking corn, going on a journey, cooking a meal or helping someone (unless they were really ill) were some of them. What will happen next? Find out on Day 4.

a Prayer

Sometimes people tried to trick Jesus, but he always knew the best thing to do.

Which would you think is most important:

• helping someone who's fallen over just at the end of playtime,

• leaving them and hurrying into class?

Lord Jesus, when I have a difficult decision, help me to know what you would do.

Jesus meets sad and lonely people

Here's what happened next in the story of the man with the crippled hand.

Isn't it better to help than to harm on the Sabbath?

Hmmph!

Stretch out your hand!

Wow! My hand is as good as new!

Read about it in **Luke chapter 6, verses 8 to 10**.

Colour in the words which you think describe how the man felt now.

happy

thankful

lonely

scared

special

surprised

Circle in the words which you think describe how the teachers of the law felt now.

sad shocked cross furious happy thoughtful

prayer time

Pretend to write the name of someone you care about on each finger, and pray for them. How does it make you feel to know that you are as special to Jesus as the man in the story?

Extra!

The man with the crippled hand must have been so excited when he found he could move his fingers again. Try this finger rhyme – it's not as easy as it sounds!

Wiggle your fingers,
One by one,
Wiggle them together,
Now wiggle your thumb.

Stretch your fingers,
One by one,
Stretch them together,
Now stretch out your thumb.

Curl your fingers,
One by one,
Curl them together
Now tuck in you thumb.

Click your fingers,
One by one,
Click them quickly
By using your thumb.

Make a plaster cast of your own hand.

You will need: an adult to help you, clay, plaster of Paris, water, a strip of card
Spread out your hand and make a clear print of it in the clay. Fix the card 'wall' round the clay. Mix the plaster of Paris and pour it into the hand print. Let it dry – it won't take long! Remove the plaster cast from the clay. Keep it as it is or paint it. No one else will have one quite like it!

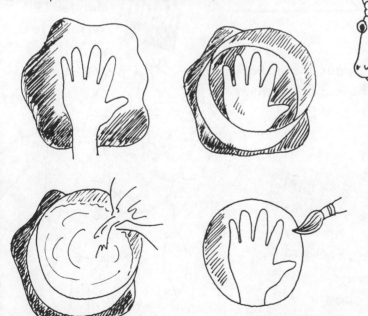

Make a list of all the things you've used your fingers and thumbs for today. You'll probably be surprised how long it is!

Jesus meets sad and lonely people

Hi! I'm Zacchaeus, but call me Zac. I have a long name but I'm a very short person! Being short used to bother me, but not any more. Not since I met Jesus, my best friend! I'm a tax collector and I didn't have any friends. I used to collect more money than I should from people. I gave some to the Romans and kept the rest for myself. I was very rich but the money didn't make me happy. I was really lonely. When I heard that Jesus was coming to town I wanted to see him.

Read about it in **Luke** chapter 19, verses 1 to 6.

prayer time

Colour in the shapes that have a dot in them to find Zac.

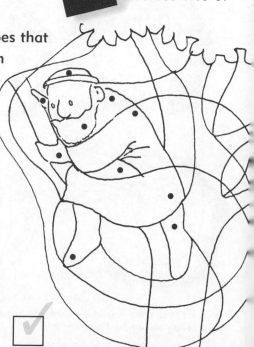

Zac said it used to bother him that he was short. Does anything bother you and make you feel sad or lonely?
Tell Jesus about it. He understands and wants to help you feel special.

Jesus meets sad and lonely people

Hello! Zac again. I want to tell you what happened next when I met Jesus. I almost fell down that tree! I could hear people grumbling about Jesus choosing me to come and eat a meal with. They said I was a bad man. Well, I was, but Jesus still cared about me! As we chatted I knew I wanted to be his friend and I felt very sorry about taking money from people. I told Jesus I'd pay everyone back four times as much as I'd taken and give half of everything else I owned to poor people.

Read what Jesus said to me in **Luke chapter 19, verses 9 and 10**.

Spot the difference. Can you find 10 differences between these two pictures?

prayer time

Saying sorry when we have done wrong things is important. Is there anything you feel sorry about and would like Jesus to help you change? Tell him about it now. Thank him for loving you and wanting to be your special friend.

Extra!

Zacchaeus found that it was much better to share his money than to keep more and more for himself.

One way of sharing money is to give some to a charity where it can be used to help people. Ask an adult to help you to decide which one, and collect your money in Zac's tree.

To make it you will need:

a cardboard tube a base for the tube green card white card brown paper glue scissors crayons or felt-tipped pens

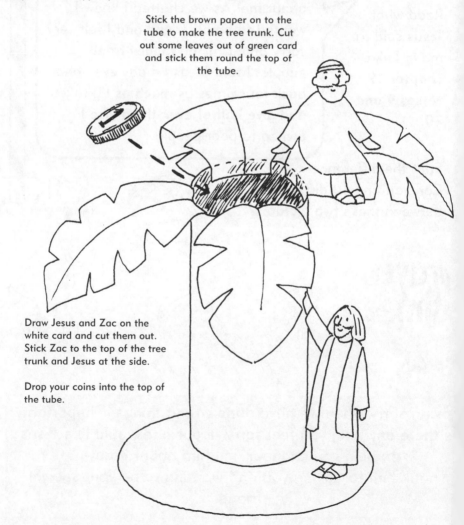

Stick the brown paper on to the tube to make the tree trunk. Cut out some leaves out of green card and stick them round the top of the tube.

Draw Jesus and Zac on the white card and cut them out. Stick Zac to the top of the tree trunk and Jesus at the side.

Drop your coins into the top of the tube.

Jacob

Isaac and Rebekah had twin sons, Esau and Jacob. Esau was Isaac's favourite and Jacob was Rebekah's. Isaac was old and couldn't see well. He called Esau, who was the eldest, and said, "Make some of my favourite food and bring it to me. Then I will give you a special blessing."

Rebekah heard Isaac. She wanted Jacob to have the special blessing. She made a plan. She cooked Isaac's favourite food. Then she helped Jacob to pretend that he was Esau. Jacob went to see Isaac.

Do you think Jacob will manage to trick Isaac?

LOOk up Genesis chapter 27, verses 19 to 23 to find out.

a rayer

E _ _ _   J _ _ _ _

Pray for your family. Say each person's name to God. Ask him to bless each one.

Esau and Jacob were very different. Make these two faces look different from each other. Write the names underneath.

Jacob

Esau was very angry when he found out about Jacob's trick. So Rebekah helped Jacob to run away. He walked for a long time. Each night he stopped to rest, lying on the ground with a stone for a pillow. One night he had a dream. In the dream, he saw a ladder going from earth to heaven. Angels were going up and down the ladder. God was standing there. He spoke to Jacob.

LOOk up Genesis chapter 28, verse 15
to find out what God said.

Jacob knew that God would be with him wherever he went. Think of some places where you go. Draw pictures of them or write them in the space.

a prayer

Lord Jesus, thank you that you are with me wherever I go.

Jacob

Jacob had been away a long time. Now he was married and had children. He wanted to see his brother Esau again. He set out on the journey with his family. He was worried that Esau was still angry with him. He sent messengers to Esau with presents. Because he was still afraid, he prayed to God.

Read **Genesis chapter 32, verses 10 to 12** to hear his prayer to God.

Think of a time when you have been afraid. Talk with someone about it.

Colour in the dots to see when we can talk to God if we are afraid.

a **prayer**

Dear God, thank you that I can talk to you when I am afraid. I know you will always listen.

Jacob

Jacob had been afraid about meeting his brother Esau again, but God helped him. Jacob walked out to meet Esau, with his family following behind. Esau was so pleased to see Jacob that he ran to meet him and hugged him. Jacob wanted to give Esau some presents, but Esau said, "No, I already have enough."

 Read **Genesis chapter 33, verses 10 to 11** to find out what happened next.

Follow the lines to find which present Jacob gave Esau.

prayer time

Esau forgave Jacob for the wrong thing he did to him. Say a prayer thanking God that he forgives us for the wrong things that we say and do.

Jacob

God said he would give land to Jacob and his family. God told him to go to the place where he had had his dream. God blessed Jacob and Jacob remembered all that God had done for him:

- God had looked after him when he was in trouble
- God had helped him when he was afraid
- God had been with him all the time.

LOOk up Genesis chapter 35, verses 14 and 15 to find out what Jacob did.

a prayer

Look at these clocks. Can you remember what you were doing at these times today? Fill in the boxes.

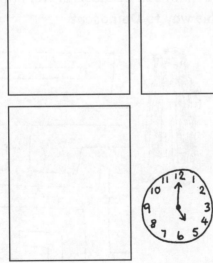

Thank you God that you have been with me today in all the things I have done.

Paul becomes a Christian

Today we start the story of a man called Paul. This was not always his name. He is called both Saul and Paul in the Bible. (Perhaps you know there is also a King in the Old Testament called Saul.)

Saul was going to a place called Damascus. Suddenly a very bright light dazzled him and he heard Jesus speaking. Saul knew about Jesus, but he did not love him. In fact, he wanted to kill everyone who believed in him. This made Jesus very sad. Jesus said, "Saul! Why are you so cruel to me?" Saul did not know who was speaking to him, and asked, "Who are you, Lord?"

Find out what Jesus replied to Saul in **Acts chapter 9, verses 3 to 6**.

Saul cannot see because of the bright light. Help him find his way to Damascus.

prayer time

Dear Jesus, thank you for loving everyone, even if they do not love you.

Paul becomes a Christian

Paul had been blinded by a bright light and could not see. God had told him to wait in a house. God told a man called Ananias to go to see Paul. Ananias was afraid. Why do you think this was? Do you think he did what God asked?

Acts chapter 9, verses 17 to 19, to find out.

Ananias called Paul by his old name. Can you remember it?

Quick Quiz

1. Paul was staying in a ...
2. Paul's old name.
3. Jesus wants ... to be his friends.
4. The Bible book where this story is found.

Thank you, God, for all the exciting stories in the Bible.

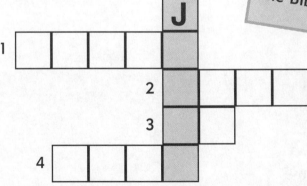

Whose name runs through all the other words?

Paul's adventures

Paul was now a Christian. But many of the Jewish people began to hate him because of his new love for Jesus. They even made plans to kill Paul.

Paul found out that the Jews were guarding the gates of the city. How would he get out?

This story is in **Acts chapter 9, verses 23 to 25**. Read **verse 25** to find out how Paul got out of the city.

Draw a picture of Paul escaping.

prayer time

God was with Paul all the time and looking after him. Think about a time when you knew that God was with you, and thank him for it.

Paul's adventures

Paul was in a place called Lystra. He was speaking to a crowd of people. Nearby was a man who had been born with crippled feet, and had never been able to walk. Paul knew that this man believed in Jesus, and that he could be healed.

Paul looked right at the man, and shouted, "Stand up!" What would happen next? Do you think that the man could stand up?

LOOk up Acts chapter 14, verses 8 to 10 to see if the man could stand.

a rayer

The man _ _ _ _ _ _ _ in Jesus. Put these words in the grid to find the missing word: **Acts believe healed Lystra Paul stand feet**

Think of someone you know who is ill and ask Jesus to bless and help them.

		A				
	L					
		P				
			S			
	F					
B						
H						

Paul's adventures

Paul was in trouble again, but this time he was with his friend Silas. They had been badly beaten up, and now they were going to be locked up in a jail.

The jailer was told to make sure that they could not escape. Find out how he did this in **Acts chapter 16, verses 23 to 24**.

Circle Paul and Silas when you have found them from the clues.

Paul is short, has straight hair and dots on his shirt.

Silas is thin, has curly hair and stripey clothes.

We don't know what they really looked like, of course, but we do know something true about them! How are they both different from the other prisoners? Read **verse 25** to see.

Tell God how happy you are to have him as your friend, no matter where you are.

Paul's adventures

Paul and Silas were in jail. It was the middle of the night, and suddenly there was an earthquake! The jailer who had locked them up was frightened and asked what he needed to do to be saved. Paul and Silas told him about the Lord Jesus. The jailer and all his family were so happy.

Acts chapter 16, verses 32 to 34 to see what they did next.

Can you see how to change this face from being sad to happy?

Now see if you can draw a happy/sad face.

a
rayer

Dear Jesus, thank you that the jailer and his family came to know you as their friend. Please be with my friends who don't know you yet.

Paul's adventures

Paul was a prisoner again. This time he was on a ship. During the journey a strong wind began to blow. It was so strong that the sailors could not control the ship. They had to let the storm carry them.

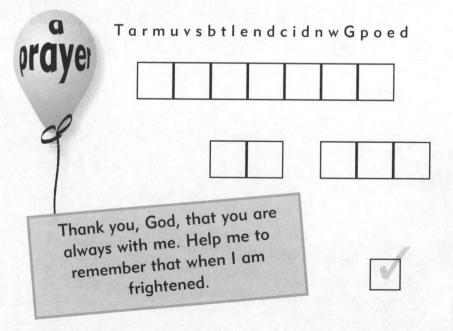

Find and read **Acts chapter 27, verses 14 to 15** in your Bible, then read **verses 18 to 20,** to see what happened next.

The sailors were frightened. Cross out every second letter to find what they should have done.

a prayer

T a r m u v s b t l e n d c i d n w G p o e d

Thank you, God, that you are always with me. Help me to remember that when I am frightened.

Paul's adventures

Paul is still on the ship, but the ship has been so battered by the wind that the sailors are going to leave it. But what about Paul and the other prisoners? The sailors wanted to kill them all! Thankfully, the captain of the ship did not want Paul to die and he came up with another plan. Read **Acts chapter 27, verses 42 to 44** to find out how Paul got to land safely.

See how much you remember about Paul's adventures. Ask a grown up to help you check your answers by looking up the Bible passages from the last 7 days. Tick the answer if you got it right.

1. What happened to Paul on the way to Damascus?

2. Who came to pray for him?

3. How did Paul escape from Damascus?

4. What was wrong with the man at Lystra?

5. Who was with Paul in prison?

6. How did the jailer become a Christian?

7. How did the sailors lighten the ship?

Father God, you are the same God who helped Paul. Thank you that you can help me too.

Extra!

Paul had many good things to say about Jesus and trusting in him. Why not make a plaque to remind you of one of them?

Here are some you could choose from. They are all from the book of Acts.

"Turn to the living God" (**chapter 14, verse 15**).

"Have faith in the Lord Jesus" (**chapter 16, verse 31**).

"God made the world and everything in it" (**chapter 17, verse 24**).

"We are God's children" (**chapter 17, verse 28**).

"I belong to God" (**chapter 27, verse 23**).

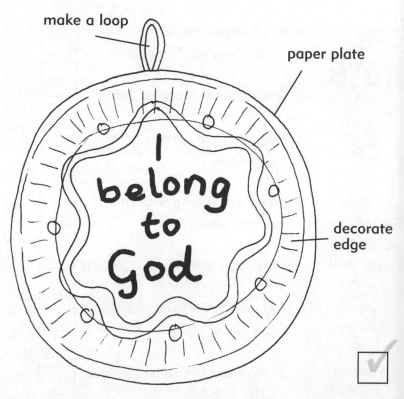

make a loop

paper plate

I belong to God

decorate edge

Decorate your plaque in any way you like and then put it somewhere where you will see it often.

All about sheep

Jesus told a story about a shepherd.

Read the beginning of it in **Luke chapter 15, verses 3 and 4**.

The shepherd knew his sheep well and noticed one was missing. Here are ten sheep. Can you see something different about each one?

a **rayer**

Jesus is like the shepherd in the story. He knows all about each one of us.

I am different from everyone else, Lord, but you know all about me, just like the shepherd knew his sheep. I am special to you. Thank you!

All about sheep

Read the next part of Jesus' story about a shepherd in **Luke chapter 15, verses 5 and 6**.

Colour in the right answers:

The shepherd found his lost sheep. YES   NO

The sheep walked home. YES   NO

The shepherd told his friends and neighbours. YES   NO

The shepherd was happy because his sheep got lost. YES   NO

The shepherd was happy because his sheep was found. YES   NO

Do you think the shepherd loved his sheep? YES   NO

a prayer

The shepherd wanted everyone to celebrate when he found his sheep. Jesus said that everyone in heaven is happy when someone is sorry for the wrong things they have done and wants to follow God.

Dear God, help me to want to be your friend. I know this will make you happy!

All about sheep

David wrote a song or psalm about sheep. He knew a lot about them because he looked after them when he was a boy. In his psalm he imagined he was a sheep and God was his shepherd.

Read some of it in **Psalm 23, verses 1 and 2**.

The shepherd knew just what the sheep needed. Look at the Bible verses again and draw the things here:

something to eat | something to drink

God knows just what we need too.
Draw some of them here:

things to eat | things to wear

somewhere to live

Prayer time

Say thank you to God for caring for you and giving you the things you need.

All about sheep

LOOk up John chapter 10, verse 14 to see something Jesus said about himself.

Fill in the spaces:

I a_ _ _ e _oo_ _ _e_ _ e_ _.

Think about what a good shepherd is like:

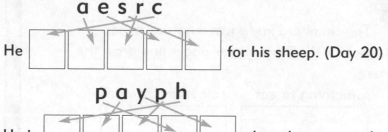

a e s r c

He [ ][ ][ ][ ][ ] for his sheep. (Day 20)

p a y p h

He is [ ][ ][ ][ ][ ] when they are not lost. (Day 21)

e n d e

He gives them what they [ ][ ][ ][ ]. (Day 22)

Jesus said something else very special too. Look at **John chapter 10, verses 2 and 3** to find out.

a m n e

He knows his sheep by [ ][ ][ ][ ].

Write your name here:

_____

a prayer

Thank you, Jesus, that you are my good shepherd, and that you know my name.

Make a good shepherd mobile.

You will need

a wire coathanger, card, wool, cotton wool, pens or crayons, glue, tracing paper, sticky tape, thick pencil.

Trace the shapes with a thick pencil. Draw several sheep. Turn the tracing paper over on the card and draw over it again to mark out the shapes. Colour and cut them out. Stick cotton wool on the sheep, making them all different if you can. Copy the verse. Fix the mobile together and hang it up.

Jesus said: "I am the good shepherd."

Jesus said I am the good shepherd

wool

sticky tape

Elijah by the river

Today we start reading some stories about Elijah. Elijah was a prophet (that's someone chosen by God to tell the people what God wanted to say to them). Many people had turned away from God and were not doing what God wanted. Elijah's job was to tell the people what God wanted them to do. Elijah told King Ahab, "Because you are not following God, there will be no rain for a long time." Then God gave Elijah some directions.

1 Kings chapter 17, verses 2 to 4 to see what God told Elijah.

God gave Elijah clear instructions. Give clear instructions to help this person get home, such as "turn left", "turn right", "straight on".

a prayer

Dear God, show me what I need to do to follow you more carefully.

Elijah by the river

God looked after Elijah, even though there was no rain and not much food. He told Elijah where to go. Elijah found a brook (a little river) and lived beside it. The ravens brought him bread and meat every morning and every evening and he drank from the brook. But the brook soon dried up as there was no rain.

Read this story in **1 Kings chapter 17, verses 5 to 7.**

Think about the food and drink that you have been given today. Draw a picture of it.

a prayer

Say a prayer thanking God for all of the food and drink that he has given you today.

Elijah by the river

Even though there was no rain and the brook had dried up, God still took care of Elijah. He told him to go to a town called Zarephath and to live there.

Elijah went, and by the town gate he met a lady who was gathering wood for a fire.

 this story in **1 Kings chapter 17, verses 8 to 12**.

Who said what? Join the words to the right person.

> Please could you bring me some bread and water?

> I only have a little flour and oil, just enough to make some bread for me and my son. That is all I have left.

Elijah wanted the lady to make him some bread. Draw a ring round the things you need to make bread.

flour yeast apples water jam bananas

Say a prayer for children who do not have enough food and drink to help them to grow.

Elijah by the river

Do you remember the lady who only had a little oil left? Elijah said to her, "Don't worry. Go home and make some bread for me first. Bring it to me. Then go home and make some more for you and your son. God has promised that the flour and the oil will never run out."

The lady went home and did as Elijah said. Did God keep his promise?

LOOk up 1 Kings chapter 17, verses 13 to 16 to find out.

The lady in the story kept her oil in a jug.
Join up the jugs that are the same.

Dear God, you really are amazing! Thank you that you always keep your promises.

Elijah on the mountains

King Ahab was still not following God. He wanted all his people to worship a statue called Baal. God sent Elijah to the people to say, "I will show you who is the true God. Let us make two piles of wood and put a sacrifice of meat on them. One will be for God and one for Baal. Let us put wood on the altars. Then we will pray for the wood to be set on fire. We will know that the God who answers is the true God." The people all thought that this was a good idea.

You can read about this in **1 Kings chapter 18, verse 24**. Elijah was asking the people to make a choice to follow God. We all have to choose to do the right thing. Think what you would do here:

a prayer

Help me, Lord, to follow you and to choose the right things to do.

Elijah on the mountains

The people had built a pile of wood for Baal. Elijah challenged the people to pray to their god to set the wood on fire. They prayed to Baal, but Baal was only a statue. They prayed harder and shouted louder but nothing happened. There was no fire. Then Elijah put stones together and the wood and meat on top. He dug a ditch around it and then poured lots of water over it so that it all got wet and there was water in the ditch. Then Elijah prayed to God.

1 Kings chapter 18, verses 38 and 39 to see what happened.

Draw the flames to show how God answered Elijah's prayer.

prayer time

Say a prayer thanking God that he is powerful and answers our prayers.

Elijah on the mountains

King Ahab told his wife Jezebel all that Elijah had done and she was very angry. She wanted to kill Elijah. Elijah ran away because he was afraid and very sad. After walking for a whole day, Elijah lay down under a tree and prayed to God. While he was asleep an angel came to Elijah and told him to eat.

Read this story in **1 Kings chapter 19, verses 5 to 9** to find out what Elijah had to eat.

Colour in the right answers.

bread

milk

water

ice cream

cake

a prayer

God provided food to make Elijah strong for the journey ahead. Draw some foods that help to make you strong:

Thank you, God, that you provide everything I need to keep me strong and healthy.

Elijah on the mountains

Elijah had been on a long journey to reach Mount Sinai and went to sleep in a cave. He was fed up and just wanted to die. He didn't know what to do. Then God spoke powerfully to Elijah.

 this story in **1 Kings chapter 19, verses 11 to 13**.

Then God told Elijah he wanted him to do some more work for him!

Can you fit these words from the stories about Elijah into the puzzle?
angel bread journey oil prophet water

Pray for people that you know who may be sad and lonely at this time. Ask God to be close to them and care for them.

Stories Jesus told

Jesus told this story:

A man had two sons. One day the younger son said "Can I have my share of your money now?" The father divided his money and gave his son half of it. A few days later the son left home and went to live in another country. The father was very sad when his son went away.

While he was living in the faraway country the son spent all his money and bought everything he wanted. He had new clothes, and had fun at lots of parties.

If you were the son sending a postcard to his father, what would you write?

What sort of picture would be on the card?

Dear Dad

Dad
Our House
Homeland

a **prayer**

Thank you, Jesus, for all the wonderful stories in the Bible.

But, oh dear ... read the story in **Luke chapter 15, verses 11 to 14** to see what happened next.

Stories Jesus told

Do you remember the son who left home? After he had spent all his money, there was a famine and hardly any food. He went to a farmer and got a job to try to earn some money.

 the story in **Luke chapter 15, verses 15 to 18.**

Colour the animals he looked after:
He looked after

Tick the right answer:

He had plenty to eat. ☐

No one gave him anything to eat. ☐

What did the son say to himself?
(Read **verse 18** again.)
How do you think he felt?

Father God, I am sorry for the wrong things
I have done.
I am sorry for _____
Thank you for loving me even when I do
wrong things.

Stories Jesus told

The son who had left home decided to go back and say he was sorry. It was a long journey and took many days. His father had been very sad and had been hoping he would come back. He was still a long way from home when his father saw him and ran to meet him. The father put his arms round his son and kissed him. The son started to say he was sorry.

Read the story in **Luke chapter 15, verses 20 to 24** to find out what the father said. Do you think he forgave him?

☐ yes ☐ no

What did he give his son? There were three things.

a prayer

Draw the food you would have for a feast.

Thank you, Father God, that you love me and care for me just like the father loved his son.

Stories Jesus told

Jesus told a story about helping people.

 it in **Luke chapter 10, verses 30 to 32.**

Fill in the missing words. (You can find them at the bottom of the page.)

There was once a man who went on a long journey. Some _____ took all his money and clothes and left him lying in the _____.

A _____ was going along the road. He saw the man lying there and walked past. He did not _____ to help the man.

Someone who worked in the temple went along the road. He crossed over and _____ at the man. Then he went on with his journey. He did not help the man who was hurt.

Prayer time

robbers

stop

looked

priest

road

Think of all the people who help you when you need it. Say thank you to God for each one of them.

Stories Jesus told

Do you remember what happened to
the man who was going on a long
journey?
Later, another man came along. He
saw the man lying in the road.
He crossed over and got off his
donkey. He was happy when he
found that the man was still alive.
He put oil on his cuts and bruises
to heal them. He wrapped
bandages round him. He lifted the man on to his donkey and
walked to an inn where they could stay. He put the man in bed
and looked after him.

Read what happened next in **Luke
chapter 10, verse 35.**

What did the man say to the innkeeper?
Write down the first letters:

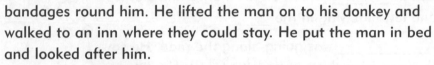

What did the
man give to
the innkeeper?
Draw them
here.

Think about
some of the
ways that
Jesus cares
for you. Say
a 'thank
you' prayer
to him.

Stories Jesus told

When Jesus finished the story he asked "who do you think was kind to the man who had been robbed and hurt?"
Put a ring round the picture of the one who was kind to the man.

the priest

the Levite
(temple worker)

the Samaritan
man on the
donkey

a prayer

Now read **Luke chapter 10, verses 36 to 37** to see what Jesus said.

Draw yourself helping someone here:

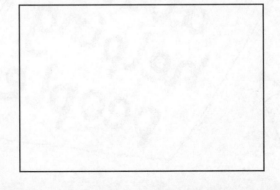

Father God,
help me to be
ready to help
whenever I
can.

Extra!

Make a story book

Fold the sheets of paper in half. Staple them together down the fold. Write the title and your name on the cover of the book.

Why not call your book **"Stories about helping people"**? You could draw pictures of Jesus' stories in the book. You could write some of your own stories too. Perhaps you could find stories about helping people in newspapers and magazines, and stick them into your book.

Read your book to one of your friends!

Elisha's poor friends

Do you have any friends whose names are similar to yours? Today we meet Elisha whose name sounds quite like Elijah who we've met before. Elisha and Elijah were friends and had the same job – to share God's message with people.

Read about a family Elisha knew in **2 Kings chapter 4, verses 1 and 2**.

Put a ✓ by the things which are true, and a ✗ by the things which are not true:

☐ The family are rich.

☐ The family are poor.

☐ Elisha says he won't help.

☐ Elisha says he will try to help.

☐ The widow only has a bottle of oil.

☐ The widow only has a loaf of bread.

☐ The family need the money for a holiday.

☐ The family need to pay a man they owe.

a prayer

Father God, thank you for sending Elisha to the widow's family when they needed help. Thank you that you know all about my family and what we need.

☑

Elisha's poor friends

Do you enjoy collecting things? Maybe you have a collection of shells, creepy crawlies or stickers!

2 Kings chapter 4, verses 3 and 4 and find out what Elisha asked the poor widow and her sons to collect.

Can you count how many jars there are here?

prayer time

Sometimes, when we don't know the end of the story, things seem puzzling. God knows the ending though and he wants us to trust him.

Talk to God about anything that puzzles you or worries you at the moment, and ask him to help you to trust him.

What will happen when they pour oil into the jars? Find out next time!

There are 18 jars.

Elisha's poor friends

Have you ever shared a bag of sweets and found there were just enough for everyone?

 what happened to the widow's oil in **2 Kings chapter 4, verses 5 and 6**.

God gave us just enough oil to fill all the jars! I must tell Elisha what has happened!

Draw the boys selling oil at the market.

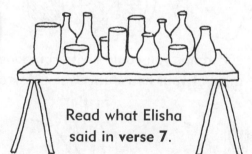

Read what Elisha said in **verse 7**.

Now you could read **Psalm 136, verses 1 to 4** and **verses 23 to 26**.

Lord, I want to say "Thank you" for all the brilliant things you do. It's very exciting! Help me to share your good news with other people.

Elisha's rich friends.

It's always exciting to receive an invitation to a party or to a friend's house for tea. Here's one for Elisha:

The Town House, Camel Street
Shunem, Israel

Dear Elisha,
Please come to dinner
at our house.
With best wishes,
Mrs Rich.

about it in **2 Kings chapter 4, verse 8**.

Colour the words you think describe the woman.

selfish
rich generous
poor
Kind mean

Colour in the food you think Elisha might have eaten at her house.

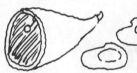

Perhaps you could invite someone to a meal at your house this week. Ask an adult first!

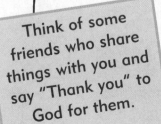

Think of some friends who share things with you and say "Thank you" to God for them.

Draw the food you would like to share with your friends if they came to a meal.

Elisha's rich friends

On Day 41 we thought about sharing a meal at a friend's house. Going to a "sleep over" at a friend's house or having a friend to stay with you is exciting too! The kind, rich woman who invited Elisha to dinner had a good idea. Read about it in **2 Kings chapter 4, verses 9 and 10**.

> Now Elisha can stay with us whenever he wants to. I hope he has everything he needs.

a prayer

Draw what the woman put in Elisha's room for him.

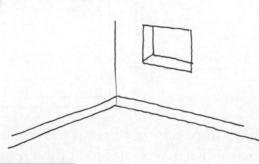

Father God, please show me how I can welcome the visitors who come to my home.

If you were having a friend to stay is there anything else you would need to get ready for them?

Elisha's rich friends

Do you remember the ten men who had a bad skin disease? (See Day 1.) Naaman in today's story had a similar disease. He lived in Syria and was in charge of the army there. One day, after a battle, his army took a girl from Israel back to Syria to be a servant for his wife. The girl heard about Naaman's disease and had an idea.

"Tell Naaman to go to Israel and see Elisha. I'm sure God will tell him how Naaman can be well again."
Naaman told the King of Syria what the girl had said.

 about it in **2 Kings 5, verses 4 to 6**.

Draw the presents Naaman took for the King of Israel.

Naaman came from another country. On television news programmes we often see people in other countries who are having a hard time. Write the name of a country which needs God's help on this television screen (ask an adult to tell you about one if you can't think of any), and pray for the people there. You can help just like the servant girl did!

Elisha's rich friends

If you were asked "Would you rather bath in scented bubbles or slimy, smelly mud?" what would you say? Naaman didn't have a choice! Elisha told him to go and wash in the River Jordan seven times and his skin disease would be better. But Naaman said:

> Oh no! Why can't Elisha just come and pray for me? Anyway, the rivers back home are much better than the smelly old River Jordan. Why can't I wash in one of those?

Naaman had sensible servants. They told him he should do what Elisha said. Read what happened in **2 Kings 5, verses 14 and 15**.

> Look, I'm well! Now I know that your God is real and powerful!

All these people helped Naaman. Draw a chain to join them together.

the girl   the king   servants   Elisha

Father God, sometimes we have to do things we don't like very much, for our own good. You knew what was best for Naaman and you know what's best for us. Please help me to trust you.

Naaman washed in the River Jordan **7** times. Here are **7** different activities with water for you to enjoy. Make sure you have an adult to help you.

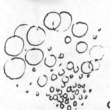

1 **Bubble Bath** Choose some special bubble bath and enjoy a frothy time.

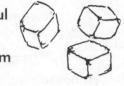

2 **Cool Cubes** Make colourful ice cubes by adding food colouring to water. Freeze them and float them in your drinks.

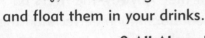

3 **All Aboard** Make a model boat out of junk and see how well it floats.

4 **Water Music** Line up some bottles and put a different amount of water in each. Play a tune on them by tapping them with a pencil. (Brighten up the water with food colouring!)

5 **Swimming** Visit your local swimming pool as a special treat.

6 **Water Colours** Paint a picture using water colour paints.

a prayer

Thank you, Lord, for the gift of water to drink, get clean in and have fun with!

7 **Car Wash** See if you can help an adult you know to wash their car!

I can pray to God

Think of some of the people you talk to.
Draw them here:

What sort of things do you talk about? Put a ring round them.

animals   school

food   *friends*   holidays

games   toys

prayer time

Did you know that you can talk to God about *anything*? That's because he made us and knows all about us. He's interested in everything we do.

 Read what David said in **Psalm 139, verses 1 to 3.**

Talk to God about what you have been doing and some of your favourite things now.

I can pray to God

David knew he could talk to God about anything, even when he felt very sad. He imagined he was like a sheep with God as his loving shepherd.

Read what he said in **Psalm 23, verse 4**.

Give the shepherd a strong rod or stick. Draw a sheep close to him.

a prayer

Thank you, God, that you are close to me. I can talk to you when I am sad and I know you will be listening.

Remember! When you feel sad, God is close by, and you can tell him all about it.

I can pray to God

Do you remember Paul? He had lots of adventures.
(Look back to Days 14 to 19.)

Paul knew that he could talk to God when he was in
trouble. God was taking care of him even when he
was shipwrecked!

Read how Paul knew this in **Acts chapter
27, verses 23 and 24**.

Draw Paul's boat on the rough sea.

prayer time

Paul was in big trouble! Whether our
troubles seem big or little, God wants
us to talk to him about them.

Have you got any troubles that you
need to talk to God about? Why don't
you do it now? If you haven't, thank
him for listening anyway.

I can pray to God

Paul was always sure God was with him even when things looked impossible. How do we know this?

LOOk up Acts chapter 16, verse 25 to see what he and Silas did when they were in prison in the middle of the night.

r y p a d e   n g a s

They ☐☐☐☐☐☐ and ☐☐☐☐ praises to God.

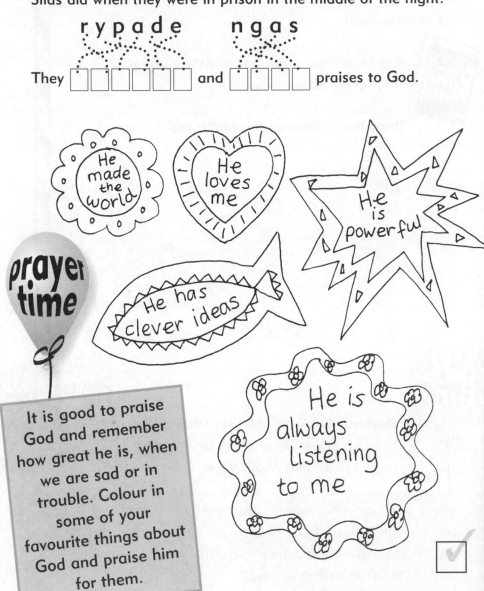

He made the world

He loves me

He is powerful

prayer time

He has clever ideas

It is good to praise God and remember how great he is, when we are sad or in trouble. Colour in some of your favourite things about God and praise him for them.

He is always listening to me

Make some treasure tubes!

Ask a grown-up to cut the tube into sections about 10 centimetres long. Cover each section with wrapping paper. Stick them together in a group.

Write something great about God on each piece of paper. Here are some ideas:
God always keeps his promises.
Jesus is the good shepherd.
God cares for me.
God is always with me.

God cares for me

Roll each paper up and hide it in one of the tubes. When you are feeling sad, take out one of the papers to remind you how great God is!

Paul writes letters

Do you remember Paul? We read about some of his adventures in the book of Acts. Although Paul did not write Acts, he did write lots of letters.

The church at Philippi was the very first one that Paul started in Greece.

Read

Philippians chapter 1, verses 3 to 5 to see how Paul began his letter to them.

Can you imagine how pleased the Philippians would have been to hear that Paul thanked God for them? The jailer who chained Paul up in prison probably read this letter! (Remind yourself of that story by looking back to Days 16 and 17.)

a prayer

Which of these letters did Paul send?
Check your answers in the contents page in the front of your Bible.

Father God, I thank you for

_____

and

_____

who make me happy.

	yes	no
From Paul to Silas	☐	☐
From Paul to the Romans	☐	☐
From Paul to the Ephesians	☐	☐
From Paul to Ananias	☐	☐

✓

Paul writes letters

Did you know that Paul wrote some parts of his letters specially to children? He reminds us that all children belong to God and he cares for every one of them.

Ephesians chapter 6, verses 1 to 3.
What else does Paul say here to children?
Is it sometimes hard to obey your parents?

☐ yes   ☐ no

If you find something difficult, talk to God about it. He always has time for you and you can talk to him at any time you like!

Draw when you can talk to God:

When I wake up ☐   ☐ In the middle of the day

In the middle of the night ☐   ☐ When I go to sleep

Please help me, God, to obey my parents, and to obey you too.

☑

All over the world!

In this book you are finding out about God and his Son Jesus, by reading the Bible.

Did you know that all over the world people read the Bible in their own languages? Can you guess which countries these Bibles are read in?

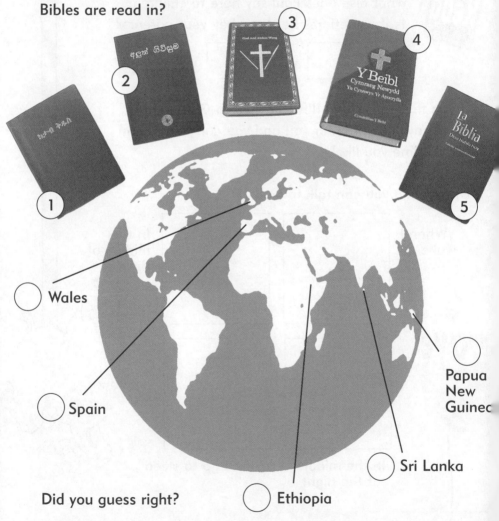

Wales

Spain

Ethiopia

Sri Lanka

Papua New Guinea

Did you guess right?

The joke and puzzle page!

Can you remember these people? You have read about all of them in this book.

• He escaped down a wall in a basket. ☐☐☐☐

• He prayed for fire to come down from heaven.
☐☐☐☐☐☐

• He climbed a tree to see Jesus.
☐☐☐☐☐☐☐☐☐

• God cured him as he bathed in a river.
☐☐☐☐☐☐

(Check your answers by looking back at Days 14, 29, 5, 44.)

What should you do if you find an elephant in your bed?
Sleep somewhere else.

Why was the footballer called Cinderella?
Because he always missed the ball.

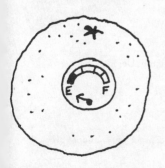

Why did the orange which fell on the floor stop rolling?
It ran out of juice.

Look out for more **Join in – Jump on!** books

Two great activity books to buy!

Like reading stories? Look out for these exciting Roller-coasters!

Bernard Bunting The Spider-Spotter!
Ro Wil...

Bernard Bunting The Worm Doctor!

PIRATE PARTY
Heather Butler

Shorty
Christine Wright

If you feel you're ready to move on from Bible Roundabouts, try Snapshots. It's great!

April - June 1999
Snap shots
Bible reading for children